STAR TREK

DEEP SPACE NINE™

MIKE W. BARR • GORDON PURCELL • TERRY PALLOT

EMANCIPATION AND BEYOND

B⬚XTREE

First published in Great Britain in 1994 by Boxtree Limited, Broadwall House, 21 Broadwall, London SE1 9PL

10 9 8 7 6 5 4 3 2 1

ISBN: 0 7522 0933 7

Printed and bound in Great Britain by Cambus Litho, East Kilbride

A CIP catalogue entry for this book is available
from the British Library

RUNABOUT *RIO GRANDE* FROM DEEP SPACE NINE TO UNIDENTIFIED VESSEL: GREETINGS.

MAKE SURE THEY KNOW WE'RE NOT HOSTILE.

WITH THEIR SIZE, THEY CAN PROBABLY DEAL WITH ANY THREAT.

OOF! WHAT'S *THAT*?

THEY'VE CAUGHT US IN A *TRACTOR BEAM*...

...BUT IT'S NOT TOO POWERFUL. I COULD BREAK IT, BUT I DON'T THINK I WILL.

JADZIA, WHY *NOT*? WE DON'T KNOW *ANY-THING* ABOUT THESE PEOPLE!

WE KNOW THEY HAVE A CLOAKING DEVICE WE CAN PIERCE, AND A TRACTOR BEAM WE CAN BREAK.

WHAT DO WE HAVE TO BE WORRIED ABOUT?

PUT THAT WAY, I SEE YOUR *POINT*.

BREATHABLE ATMOSPHERE. THE HANDLE ON THAT HATCH SEEMS BUILT FOR HUMANOID HANDS.

I EXPECT OUR "HOSTS" ARE MONITORING *US*, AS WELL.

YOU ARE *CORRECT*, ALIEN MALE. WE ENTERED INTO NO COMMUNICATION WITH YOU....

...FOR WE NEEDED TO ASCERTAIN IF YOU WERE ALLIED WITH OUR *PUR-SUERS*.

YOU WILL DROP YOUR WEAPONS, TO PROVE YOU MEAN US NO HARM.

HOW DO WE KNOW *YOU* MEAN *US* NO HARM?

YOU MUST ACCEPT OUR WORD...FOR ...FOR...

MARD...

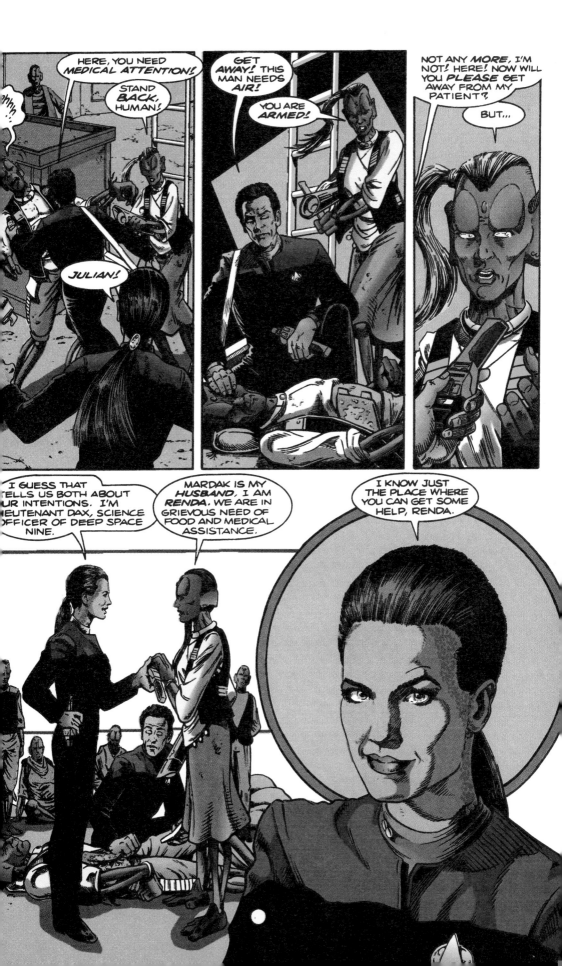

COMMANDER, A MESSAGE FROM LIEUTENANT DAX.

I'LL TAKE IT HERE, MAJOR.

DAX? EVERYTHING ALL RIGHT WITH THE MISSION?

FINE, BENJAMIN. AS A MATTER OF FACT, JULIAN AND I ARE BRINGING SOME VISITORS.

VISITORS? DAX, WHAT KIND OF--

INCREASED NEUTRINO EMISSIONS FROM THE WORMHOLE, COMMANDER.

"...WHOEVER THESE 'VISITORS' ARE... THEY'VE ARRIVED."

E THANK YOU FOR YOUR NDNESS, COMMANDER KO. MY PEOPLE ND I ARE FLEEING A RACE OF PRESSORS. WE QUEST ASYLUM.

I'LL HAVE TO TALK TO MY SUPERIORS ABOUT THAT, MARDAK, IN THE MEANTIME, YOU AND YOUR PEOPLE PLEASE FEEL FREE TO AVAIL YOURSELVES OF OUR SERVICES...

SUCH AS THEY ARE.

INTERESTING TECHNOLOGY, CHIEF?

JUST THE *OPPOSITE*, ODO. I'M SURPRISED THIS RATTLETRAP MADE IT HALF AS FAR AS THEY SAY IT DID.

BUT THE *INSIDE* IS INTRIGUING; IT'S ALL FITTED WITH *BERTHS*, LIKE A *HOSPITAL SHIP*

--THOUGH THEIR SICKBAY IS A *JOKE*--

OR A *TRANSPORT* SHIP...

OR A *CARGO* SHIP, PERHAPS-- IF ITS CARGO WAS *PEOPLE?*

PERHAPS.

AND YOU SAY HESE MARKS CAME FROM...?

THE *REACTOR GRID* OF OUR SHIP; I STUPIDLY FELL AGAINST IT.

BASHIR TO SISKO. COMMANDER, MAY I HAVE A WORD WITH YOU?

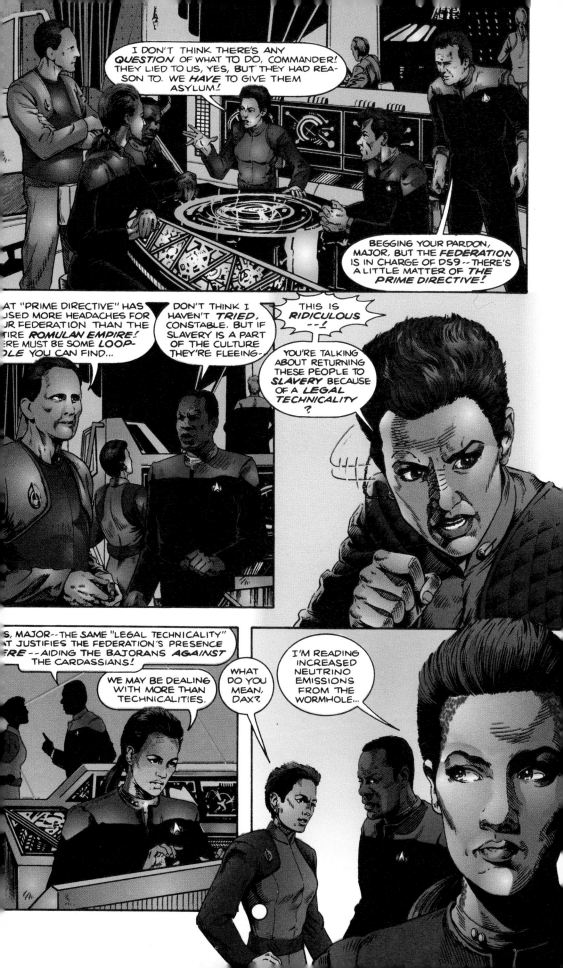

LIEUTENANT, I WAS *NOT* ATTEMPTING TO MISLEAD YOU! THE COORDINATES I GAVE YOU ARE THOSE OF OUR *HOME PLANET*--THE PLANET WE CHIARAN ARE SAID TO HAVE FIRST COME FROM, EONS AGO.

I'LL DO WHAT I CAN, MARDAK, BUT DON'T EXPECT ANY MIRACLES.

SORRY FOR THE DELAY, CAPTAIN ROGON, I'M SURE YOU'LL AGREE OUR STRINGENT MEASURES ARE NECESSARY FOR YOUR CREW'S HEALTH AS WELL AS--

WHERE IS *SISKO?*

THE COMMANDER AWAITS YOU IN OUR CONFERENCE ROOM *MAY* I ESCORT YOU?

I *NEED* NO "ESCORT!"

IT'S OUR *POLICY,* CAPTAIN.

OUT! HONEST QUARK'S IS NO PLACE FOR TROUBLEMAKERS!

BUT YOU *CHEATED!* THAT WAS ALL THE MONEY I *HAD!*

PLEASE, MASTERS-- HELP ME! HE *STOLE* MY POSSESSIONS!

I DID NO SUCH *THING,* HE LOST IT AT THE DABO TABLES! LOOK, I DON'T WANT ANY *TROUBLE...!*

YOU WANTED YOUR FREEDOM, SLAVE--NOW YOU *HAVE* IT!

WHAK

THE FREEDOM TO MAKE YOUR OWN *MISTAKES*, AND *RUIN* YOUR OWN LIFE!

WELCOME TO QUARK'S GENTLEMEN--OUR *FROZEN NEBULAS* ARE KNOWN THROUGHOUT THE *QUADRANT.* PERHAPS ONE ON THE *HOUSE...?*

COMMANDER SISKO, CAPTAIN--

I AM *ROGON.*

I AM SISKO. MAY I PRESENT--

MY *GOD--!*

MOTHER.

MY SON.

I *THOUGHT* YOU WOULD LIKE TO SEE EACH OTHER AGAIN.

SHALL WE BEGIN...?

WE ARE READY.

MOTHER, SIT DOWN.

MY RIGHT IS NOT TO SIT, MY RIGHT IS TO SERVE.

I SEE NO REAL *PURPOSE* TO THIS DISCUSSION, COMMANDER. DOES YOUR "PRIME DIRECTIVE" NOT FORBID YOU FROM INTERFERING WITH OTHER CULTURES?

IT DOES, BUT--

IT WOULD BE A *SHAME* IF OUR CIVILIZATIONS CAME TO WAR OVER SUCH A CLEAR-CUT MATTER, WOULD IT NOT?

I'M NOT SURE IT'S THAT CLEAR, ROGON.

ESE ARE ALL ...ALITIES...

...THEY DO NOT DEAL WITH THE *MIND*...OR THE *SOUL*.

I BEG PARDON, MASTER, I WAS NOT GIVEN *LEAVE* TO SPEAK.

NO OFFENSE WAS GIVEN. I *GRANT* THAT LEAVE.

YOUR FATHER WAS HAPPY IN HIS PLACE. HIS FATHER WAS HAPPY THUS. I AM HAPPY. WHY CAN YOU NOT BE?

BECAUSE WE ARE *SLAVES*, MOTHER.

ALL ARE SLAVES, SON. CAPTAIN ROGON SERVES CHIARA. COMMANDER SISKO SERVES HIS FEDERATION. NONE OF US ARE FREE.

NOT ULTIMATELY, NO--

RETURN TO US.

YOU CHIARANS, DO YOU HEAR? YOUR REBELLION DISSOLVES THE FABRIC OF THE SOCIETY WE ALL LOVE.

RETURN TO US, AND THIS INCIDENT WILL BE FORGOTTEN. PERSIST, AND YOU HAVE DOOMED CHIARA. WE WILL WAIT TWELVE HOURS BEFORE TAKING FURTHER ACTION, NO LONGER.

DON'T LISTEN TO HIM--OR TO HER--OR EVEN TO ME! LISTEN TO YOUR SOULS, THE VOICES THAT HAVE CRIED FOR FREEDOM FOR YEARS--

STAR TREK®
DEEP SPACE NINE™
...BECAUSE IT'LL BE TOO BAD FOR ANYTHING THAT GETS IN MY WAY!

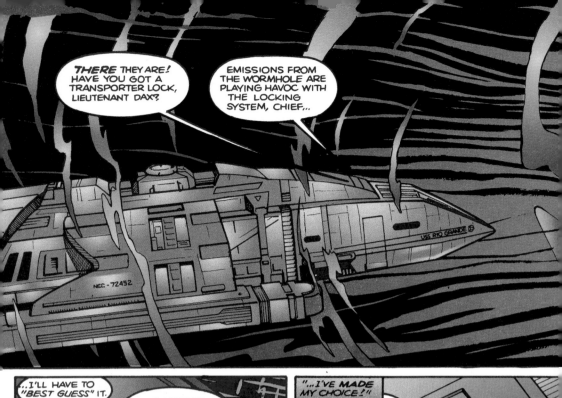

THERE THEY ARE! HAVE YOU GOT A TRANSPORTER LOCK, LIEUTENANT DAX?

EMISSIONS FROM THE WORMHOLE ARE PLAYING HAVOC WITH THE LOCKING SYSTEM, CHIEF,...

NCC-72452

USS RIO GRANDE

..I'LL HAVE TO "BEST GUESS" IT.

YOU BETTER GUESS FAST! IF IT COMES TO CHOOSING BETWEEN THE LIVES OF TWO TERRORISTS OR THE WORMHOLE...

"...I'VE MADE MY CHOICE!"

THEY'RE PURSUING US, NOMOK!

"...FREEING OUR PEOPLE FOREVER!"

THEY'RE ABOUT TO *EXPLODE*, CHIEF.

WE KNEW THEY WOULD, MARDAK! HOW MUCH LONGER?

GANGES

SECONDS! SECONDS UNTIL THE INVERTED POWER CONDUITS *EXPLODE...*

NOT IN *HERE*, THEY'RE NOT...!

REVERSE-- oh.

WELCOME ABOARD, GENTLEMEN.

YOU'RE UNDER ARREST.

"STATION LOG, SUPPLEMENTAL: DAX AND O'BRIEN ARE RETURNING WITH MARDAK AND NOMOK."

WHAT DID YOU THINK YOU WERE DOING?

SECURING OUR PEOPLE'S FREEDOM, COMMANDER SISKO.

EXPLAIN.

CAPTAIN ROGON WISHES TO RETURN US TO SLAVERY ON OUR HOME PLANET OF CHIARA, ON THE GAMMA QUADRANT SIDE OF THE WORMHOLE.

AND YOU THOUGHT TO ELIMINATE THAT BY ELIMINATING THE WORMHOLE, IS THAT RIGHT?

...IT IS *YOU* WHO GAVE OFFENSE! IT IS *YOU* WHO WILL APOLOGIZE...

CAPTAIN--!

...*UNDER*CAPTAIN!

I...APOLOGIZE.

I DIDN'T *HEAR* THAT.

MAJOR--!

OH, ALL RIGHT.

AIN, I KNOW WANT THE ONERS TURNED TO *YOU*, T--

NOT AT ALL, COMMANDER. THIS IS YOUR JURISDICTION, AFTER ALL. I APOLOGIZE FOR THE ACTIONS OF MY SUBORDINATE, HE IS *YOUNG*.

SO IS *MINE*, THANK YOU, CAPTAIN.

CAPTAIN, WHY DO YOU TAKE THE COMMANDER'S *SIDE*?

YOU *ARE* YOUNG, TO ASK SUCH A QUESTION. ATTEND: WHEN THEY FIRST ARRIVED, THE SYMPATHIES OF SISKO AND HIS PEOPLE WERE CLEARLY WITH THE *SLAVES*.

NEVER BEEN MUCH ON [A]NY. JAKE'S MOTHER, [SH]E WAS THE GARDENER.

ANY FURTHER WORD WHETHER OR NOT THIS [PLA]NET IS ACTUALLY THE *HOME* [OF T]HE CHIARAN RACE -- THE [PL]ANET THE SLAVES WISH TO EMIGRATE TO?

THERE'S NO EVIDENCE THAT IT *ISN'T*--THOUGH I LIKE MY PROOF MORE ON THE *POSITIVE* SIDE.

[Y]OU *COULD* JUST [LE]T THEM *ESCAPE*, YOU KNOW.

I *COULD*--BUT ROGON WOULD CUT ME A NEW BLOW-[H]OLE...WITH THE FEDERATION'S *BLESSING*.

BENJAMIN, YOU HAVE THE LIVES OF EVERYONE ABOARD THIS *STATION* TO WORRY ABOUT...YOU CAN'T TAKE ON THE WORRIES OF THE ENTIRE *QUADRANT*.

I DON'T *INTEND* TO, DAX...

...BUT THE CHIARANS-- SLAVES *AND* SLAVERS--ARE BOTH *ABOARD* DS9. THAT *MAKES* THEIR WORRIES MINE.

GOOD LUCK WITH YOUR FLOWERS.

HAVE TO *EXPLAIN* MOTHER, YOU DON'T UNDER--

I UNDERSTAND *THIS* = I WISH MY SON TO OUTLIVE HIS *MOTHER.*

A REMARKABLE WOMAN. SHE REMINDS ME OF MY OWN MOTHER.

I WISH SHE REMINDED ME OF MINE.

WHAT?

AH, OF COURSE.

, CAPTAIN SON. WELCOME O QUARK'S.

THANK YOU. MY MEN SPEAK VERY HIGHLY OF YOUR HOSPITALITY, MR. QUARK.

HOW VERY KIND. A NOBLE CREW, ONE AND ALL! WE'VE A NUMBER OF CHIARAN DISHES PREPARED FOR YOU, RIGHT THIS WAY!

ROM! A BOTTLE OF *SAURIAN BRANDY!* THE *GOOD* ONE, NOT THE STUFF FROM THE BAR!

Y-YES, QUARK!

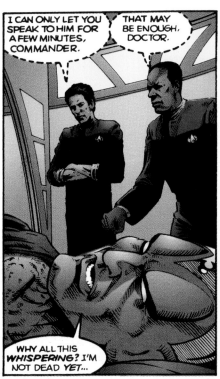

I CAN ONLY LET YOU SPEAK TO HIM FOR A FEW MINUTES, COMMANDER.

THAT MAY BE ENOUGH, DOCTOR.

WHY ALL THIS WHISPERING? I'M NOT DEAD YET...

...THOUGH THAT'S THROUGH NO FAULT OF THOSE UNGRATEFUL SLAVES!

YOU THINK MARDAK'S MEN WERE BEHIND THIS, ROGON?

WHO ELSE, COMMANDER?

...CAPTAIN ROGON'S WORST ENEMY DOESN'T WANT HIM DEAD WITH THAT KIND OF PASSION!

I FEAR MY UNDERCAPTAIN IS CORRECT, COMMANDER.

MARDAK HAS SAID HE'D BE WILLING TO PAY ANY PRICE FOR FREEDOM...

...I WONDER IF HE TRULY COUNTED THE COST.

I INTEND TO ASK HIM.

I WISH TO SPEAK TO HIM MYSELF, COMMANDER

E YOU *SATISFIED*, RDAK? YOUR CRUSADE S COST THE LIFE OF YOUR OWN *MOTHER*.

YOUR *"PRIME DIRECTIVE"* MAY FORBID YOU FROM *AIDING* US, COMMANDER, BUT WE...WE WILL *NOT* TURN BACK.

NOR WILL YOU BE *REQUIRED* TO, MARDAK...

...MY PRONOUNCEMENT WILL BECOME OFFICIAL AS SOON AS I HAVE CONTACTED CHIARA, BUT I WILL TELL YOU NOW, TO *CEASE* THIS SENSELESS VIOLENCE -- I HEREBY *GRANT* YOU YOUR FREEDOM!

WHAT?

I GIVE NO VALIDITY TO YOUR *CAUSE*, I ONLY WISH TO PRESERVE CHIARAN *SOCIETY*.

AND YOUR *OWN LIFE* AS WELL, EH, ROGON?

I HAVE LOST MORE BLOOD THAN YOUR BODY *CONTAINS* IN SERVICE TO CHIARA! DO YOU THINK ONLY THE CONSCIENCE OF A *SLAVE* CARES FOR THE FATE OF HIS HOME?

IF EXPELLING YOU AND YOUR KIND BRINGS *PEACE* TO CHIARA, IT IS A PRICE *WELL PAID*...

...WERE IT IN MY POWER, I WOULD SACRIFICE YOU *ALL* FOR THE RETURN OF YOUR *MOTHER*.

DO YOU STAND READY RECEIVE YOUR FREEDOM, MARDAK?

YOU CANNOT GRANT US THAT WHICH IS OURS BY *NATURE*, ROGON -- YOU MAY ONLY *ACKNOWLEDGE* IT!

MARDAK, THIS IS *NOT* A TIME TO STAND ON TECHNICALITIES.

YOU ARE CORRECT, COMMANDER.

WE ARE READY, CAPTAIN.

THEN LET IT BE KNOWN THAT--

WHOOM!

SISKO TO OPS! WHAT'S GOING ON?

KIRA HERE, SIR. WE'RE UNDER *ATTACK*...

...BY THE EMANCIPATOR!

FIELD TRIP

▶ Writer: MIKE W. BARR
▶ Artists: ROB DAVIS & TERRY PALLOT
▶ Letterer: PATRICK OWSLEY
▶ Editor: TOM MASON & MARK PANICCIA

"STATION LOG, PERSONAL: I AM ESCORTING KEIKO O'BRIEN'S CLASS ON A FIELD TRIP TO THE OTHER SIDE OF THE WORMHOLE -- A PLEASANT CHANGE FROM THE RIGORS OF COMMAND."

THANK YOU FOR COMING, COMMANDER-- THE CHILDREN REALLY ENJOYED IT.

IT WAS MY PLEASURE, MRS. O'BRIEN...

"...BUT I HOPE JAKE WAS ABLE TO ENJOY IT. IT CAN BE INHIBITING FOR A BOY, TO BE THE ONLY STUDENT WITH A PARENT ALONG."

COMMANDER SISKO TO CAPTAIN NOG. MY TRICORDER SHOWS ALIEN BEINGS AHEAD.

I CONFIRM THOSE READINGS, SCIENCE OFFICER.

COMMANDER--!

HOW'S DAD?!

CRZZZT

THEY'RE BOTH STILL ALIVE, BUT THEIR BREATHING IS VERY SHALLOW. SOME-ONE BRING ME THE MEDICAL KIT, PLEASE.

MAYBE WE SHOULD GO BACK...

ACCORDING TO THE READINGS, OUR POWER RESERVE IS VERY LOW, I DON'T THINK WE COULD MAKE A SOFT LANDING. WE'D BETTER TRY TO MAKE IT INTO THE WORMHOLE BEFORE OUR ORBIT DECAYS.

WHICH WAY'S THAT?

WHERE *ARE* THEY?

HEY'RE *LATE* -- IT'S NOT KE KEIKO T'BE LATE! CAN'T E SEND ANOTHER RUNABOUT AFTER THEM?

WE DON'T HAVE ONE TO *SPARE*, CHIEF. THE *RIO GRANDE* IS IN USE, AND THE *GANGES* IS BEING SERVICED.

THERE'S *NO SIGN*? NO INCREASED NEUTRINO ACTIVITY FROM THE WORMHOLE? MAYBE THIS *MONITOR* NEEDS TO BE RECALIBRATED.

YOU KNOW *DAX* WOULD NEVER ALLOW HER EQUIPMENT TO GET IN THAT STATE.

SHOULD'VE GONE WITH HER! IF ANYTHING'S *HAPPENED* --!

I'LL TELL MAINTENANCE TO PUT TOP PRIORITY ON THE *GANGES*. TRY NOT TO *WORRY*, CHIEF...

"...I'M SURE EVERYTHING'S FINE."

MRS. O'BRIEN, WHAT ARE WE *GONNA DO*?

WE ARE *NOT* GOING TO PANIC. EVERYONE REMAIN *CALM*.

...BUT WITH OUR *GUIDANCE* AND *TELEMETRY* SYSTEMS OUT, WE HAVE NO WAY OF FINDING IT. AND WE DON'T HAVE ENOUGH *POWER* TO SEARCH FOR IT.

SCIENCE OFFICER SISKO, I AM READING NO ACTIVITY FROM THE WORMHOLE...

NOG, THIS ISN'T A *GAME* ANY--

NOG, THAT'S IT!

YOU'VE HAD A *WONDERFUL* IDEA!

I *HAVE?* I--I DIDN'T *MEAN* TO...

THE WORMHOLE EMITS *NEUTRINOS!* THE *RUNABOUT'S* SYSTEMS ARE DOWN, BUT IF LIEUTENANT DAX'S *TRICORDER* CAN DETECT THE ACCUMULATION OF NEUTRINOS...

...*THERE!* HEADING MARK 5321! DO WE HAVE ENOUGH POWER TO GET THERE?

I THINK JUST *BARELY...!*

IT SHOULD BE *HERE!* IF IT'S *NOT...*

PICKPOCKET

▶ Writer: JOHN VORNHOLT
▶ Artists: ROB DAVIS & TERRY PALLOT
▶ Letterer: DAVE LANPHEAR
▶ Editors: TOM MASON & MARK PANICCIA

WAS A SLOW
Y AT QUARK'S.

HI, QUARK. SAY, WHERE IS EVERYBODY?

FUNNY YOU SHOULD ASK THAT, DOCTOR BASHIR.

WHERE IS YOUR *COMMUNICATOR BADGE*?

MY GOODNESS! I HAD IT JUST A *MOMENT* AGO. I HAVE TO GO *LOOK* FOR IT.

RELAX, DOCTOR, YOU DIDN'T LOSE IT. THAT'S WHY THIS PLACE IS EMPTY.

THERE'S A PICKPOCKET WORKING THE PROMENADE, AND HE'S *STEALING* EVERYONE'S VALUABLES BEFORE THEY CAN COME IN *HERE* AND LOSE THEM *GAMBLING*!

HAVE YOU TOLD ODO?

ODO IS AWAY AT A SECURITY CONFERENCE, OR ELSE HE'D MAKE QUICK WORK OF THIS *CROOK*! DON'T TELL HIM I SAID SO!

I HATED TO DO IT. SHE WAS SO *GOOD* AT HER PROFESSION.

WHAT ABOUT THIS LITTLE FELLA?

LATER THAT DAY AFTER ODO'S RETURN...

IT'S ABOUT TIME YOU GOT BACK.

YES, CONSTABLE. DID YOU HEAR WE *CAPTURED* A DANGEROUS *PICKPOCKET* WHILE YOU WERE GONE?

YOU'VE DONE MORE THAN THAT.

THE WOMAN WAS A NOTED RENEGADE, AND THE BABY HAD BEEN KIDNAPPED. HIS RIGHTFUL PARENTS ARE COMING HERE TO GET HIM.

I ALWAYS KNEW I WOULD BE A HERO!

NEXT TIME YOU GO AWAY, CONSTABLE, YOU SHOULD *DEPUTIZE* US TO TAKE OVER.

I'LL NEVER LEAVE AGAIN.

NOT AGAIN...

AFTERNOON, DOCTOR... AFTERNOON, OLD MAN.

BENJAMIN... IS EVERYTHING... ALRIGHT?

EVERYTHING'S FINE... *JUST FINE.*

WELL, DOCTOR, WHAT DID YOU MAKE OF *THAT?*

IT APPEARS THAT YOUR PREVIOUS CONCERNS ABOUT THE COMMANDER'S *MENTAL STATE* ARE NO LONGER RELEVANT... I WONDER

I DON'T UNDERSTAND IT, JULIAN. FOR THE PAST FEW DAYS HE'S COME OUT OF HERE LOOKING *SHATTERED.* HE WOULDN'T TALK ABOUT IT... *NOT EVEN TO ME.* THAT'S WHEN I ASKED YOU TO CONSIDER A FORMAL MEDICAL REPORT--

JADZIA... HE'S FORGOTTEN TO ERASE--

WHATEVER HE'S BEEN GOING THROUGH IN THERE DID NOT SEEM TO BE DOING HIM ANY GOOD... UNTIL NOW. I WISH I KNEW WHAT WAS BEHIND THAT DOOR.

...DO YOU *REALLY* WANT TO KNOW WHAT HAS BEEN GOING ON, JULIAN?

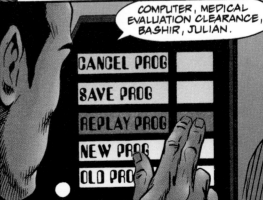

COMPUTER, MEDICAL EVALUATION CLEARANCE, BASHIR, JULIAN.

CANCEL PROG

SAVE PROG

REPLAY PROG

NEW PROG

OLD PRO

PROGRAM 359

► Writers: COLIN CLAYTON & CHRIS DOWS
► Artists: ROB DAVIS & TERRY PALLOT
► Letterer: PATRICK OWSLEY
► Editor: MARK PANICCIA

THE SARATOGA...

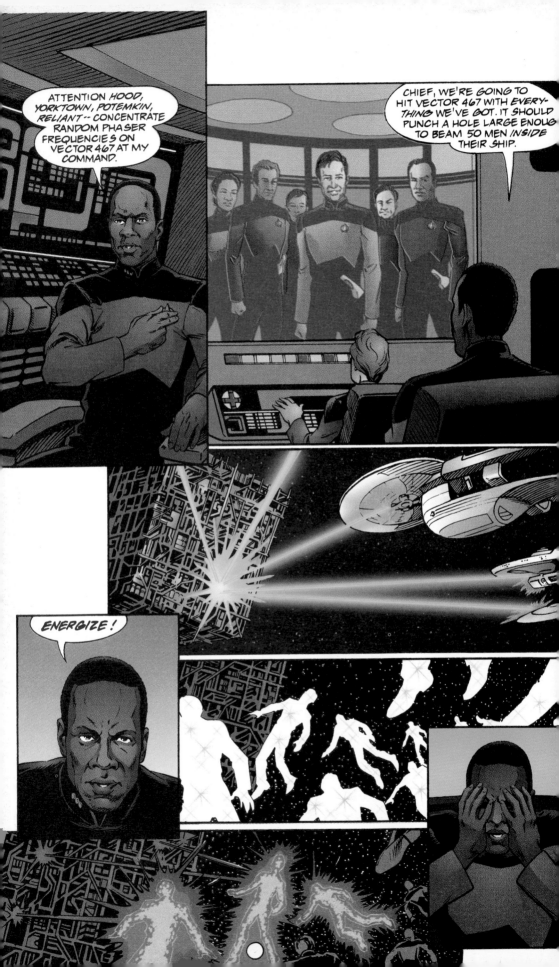

I OUGHT TO BE ANNOYED AT YOU INVADING MY PRIVACY IN THIS MANNER... *EXPLAIN YOURSELF, DOCTOR.*

WELL... I...

WE WERE JUST DECIDING WHETHER TO COMPILE A FORMAL MEDICAL REPORT ON YOU. WE'VE BEEN CONCERNED.

REALLY? WHY? I DON'T BELIEVE YOU WILL FIND ME UNFIT OR INCAPACITATED FOR THIS COMMAND, JADZIA.

DON'T PLAY GAMES, BENJAMIN. ALL WE'VE JUST SEEN... YOU IN COMMAND, THE NEW TACTICS... WHAT GOOD HAS IT DONE YOU? YOU CAN'T CHANGE THE PAST! THE OUTCOME WAS JUST THE SAME.

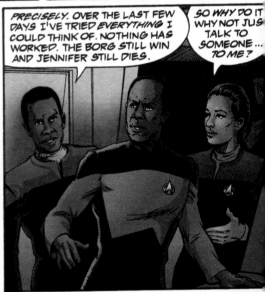

PRECISELY. OVER THE LAST FEW DAYS I'VE TRIED EVERYTHING I COULD THINK OF. NOTHING HAS WORKED. THE BORG STILL WIN AND JENNIFER STILL DIES.

SO WHY DO IT WHY NOT JUS TALK TO SOMEONE... TO ME?

I KNOW NOW FOR SURE THAT I -- THAT *NO ONE* COULD HAVE DONE *ANYTHING.* THAT KNOWLEDGE HAS FINALLY GIVEN ME THE PEACE OF MIND I'VE WANTED FOR SO LONG.

I KNOW I CAN'T CHANGE THE PAST, OLD MAN. AND I FEEL BETTER FOR IT.

COMPUTER... ERASE PROGRAM 359.

THE E

WORKING VACATION
THAT'S OUTRAGEOUS! YOU KNOW YOU CAN'T TRUST THOSE... THOSE...
...MURDERERS!
STAR TREK®
DEEP SPACE NINE™
Based on STAR TREK Created by Gene Roddenberry and STAR TREK: DEEP SPACE NINE Created by Rick Berman & Michael Piller
writer LEN STRAZEWSKI
penciller ROB DAVIS
inker TERRY PALLOT
letterer PATRICK OWSLEY
editor MARK PANICCIA

OH, PARDON ME FOR ENTERING! I BEEPED SEVERAL TIMES BUT... YOU'VE NOT CHANGED!

NO, I'M STILL THE SAME AS I WAS.

'VE PROGRAMMED SEVERAL PPROPRIATE CHOICES FOR UR ARRIVAL ON OUR HOME ORLD. THEY ARE VERY TRACTIVE AND COMFORTABLE!

I DON'T THINK SO, STEWARD, TELL ME ABOUT THE NEGOTIATION?

HOW ABOUT THIS ONE? THE COLOR MATCHES YOUR EYES!

THE NEGOTIATION? IT AFFIRMS THE SACRED CONTRACT BETWEEN OUR PEOPLES--ESTAB-LISHES THE CLASS AND RACE RESPONSIBILITY.

RACE RESPONSIBILITY? YOU ARE NOT ALL THE SAME RACE?

NO, THERE ARE DIFFERENCES, BUT THEY PROBABLY ARE NOT APPARENT TO OFF-WORLDERS.

MANY GENERATIONS AGO, WE SETTLED OUR ENMITY WITH THE NEGOTIATION OF COMBAT AND THE PRICE OF OUR LOSS IN THE FIRST NEGOTIATION WAS THE CONTRACT.

AND YOU'VE *NEVER* WON A NEGOTIATION?

F COURSE NOT. NLIKE THE MASTER LASS, WE ARE NOT RAINED FOR OMBAT. WE ARE RAINED TO SERVE. THUS THE CONTRACT DECREES!

THAT'S NOT FAIR! THAT MEANS THE NEGOTIATION IS SUICIDE FOR YOUR PEOPLE!

YES, BUT THAT IS NONE OF AN OFF-WORLDER'S AFFAIR, IS IT? HOW ABOUT THIS ONE?

ABSOLUTELY NOT!

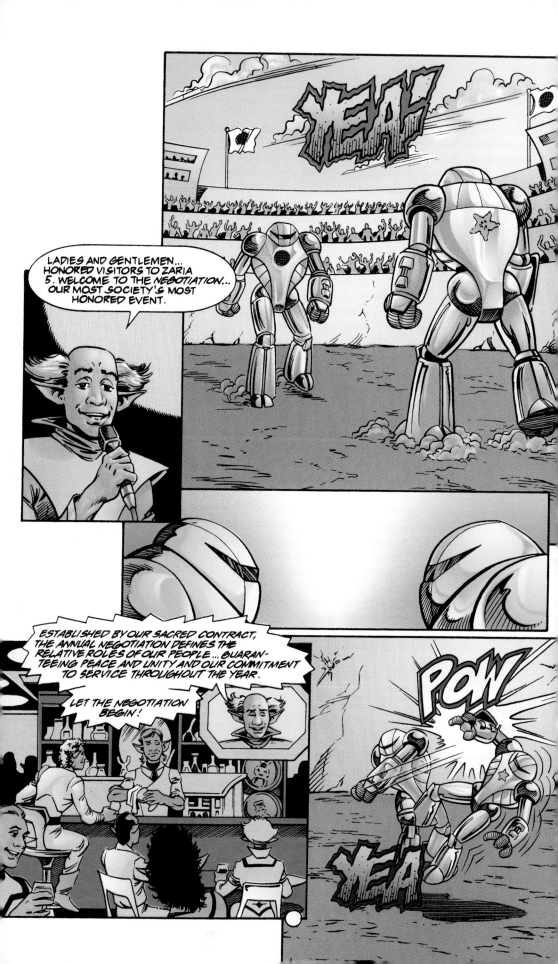

BZZAP!

ROAR!

Ah, ISN'T IT AS I SAID! IT IS WONDERFUL TO WATCH THE RIGHTNESS OF OUR SYSTEM UPHELD IN COMBAT.

Hmmm-hmmm!

YEAH, RIGHT. BUT NOT MUCH OF A FIGHT SO FAR!

ROAR!

WHAM

WHAM WHAM WHAM

ROAR!